THE MAGICAL

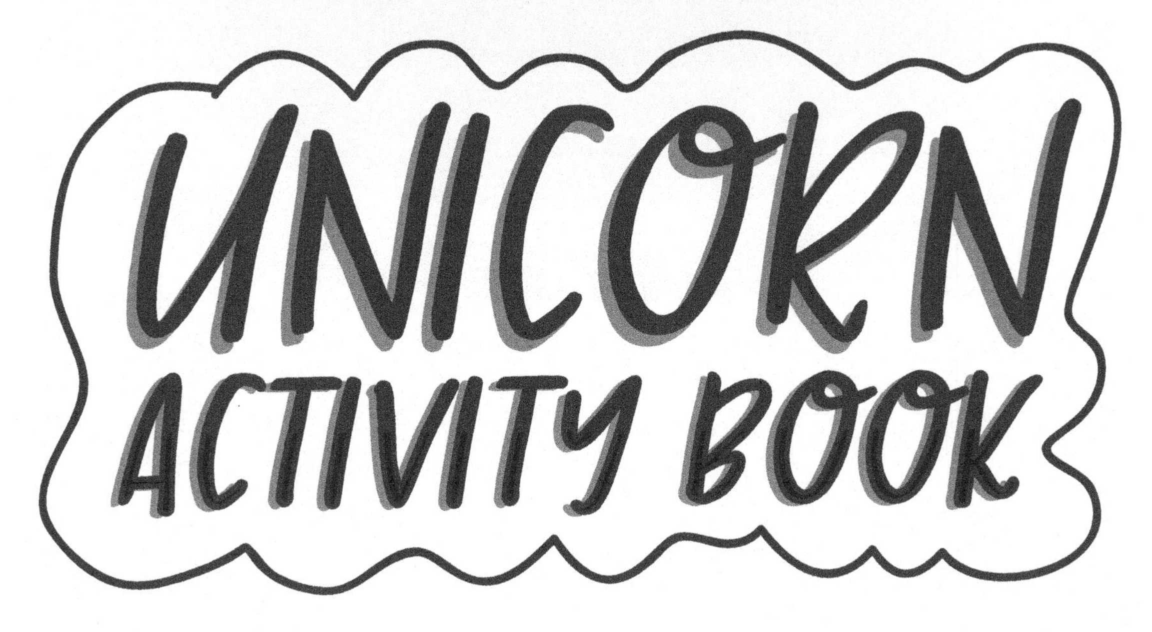

EMAIL US AT

modernkidpress@gmail.com

TO GET FREE EXTRAS!

Just title the email "Unicorn Activities"

And we will send some extra

surprises your way!

THIS MAGICAL BOOK BELONGS TO:

UP IN THE CLOUDS!

FIND THE 3 DIFFERENCES IN THESE TWO SCENES.

Use your imagination!

DRAW A PICTURE OF THE PRINCESS WHO LIVES IN THE CASTLE.

WORD SEARCH

FIND THE UNICORN NAMES BELOW!

S	G	E	S	P	A	R	K	L	E	U	D
H	L	E	P	D	G	A	P	B	L	N	O
I	I	O	R	Y	O	I	I	Q	U	I	M
M	T	T	I	P	L	N	N	X	N	C	D
M	T	M	N	M	D	B	K	C	A	O	R
E	E	M	K	D	E	O	Y	N	Y	R	K
R	R	A	L	Z	N	W	Q	H	O	N	P
Z	V	I	E	A	V	I	O	L	E	T	H

SPARKLE
GLITTER
GOLDEN
LUNA
PINKY
RAINBOW
SHIMMER
SPRINKLE
UNICORN
VIOLET

A LOVELY DAY FOR FROLICKING IN THE FIELD!

HOW MANY CROWNS DO YOU COUNT?

YOUR ANSWER:

ANSWER: 4

Use your imagination!

DECORATE THE DONUTS FOR A UNICORN BREAKFAST PARTY!

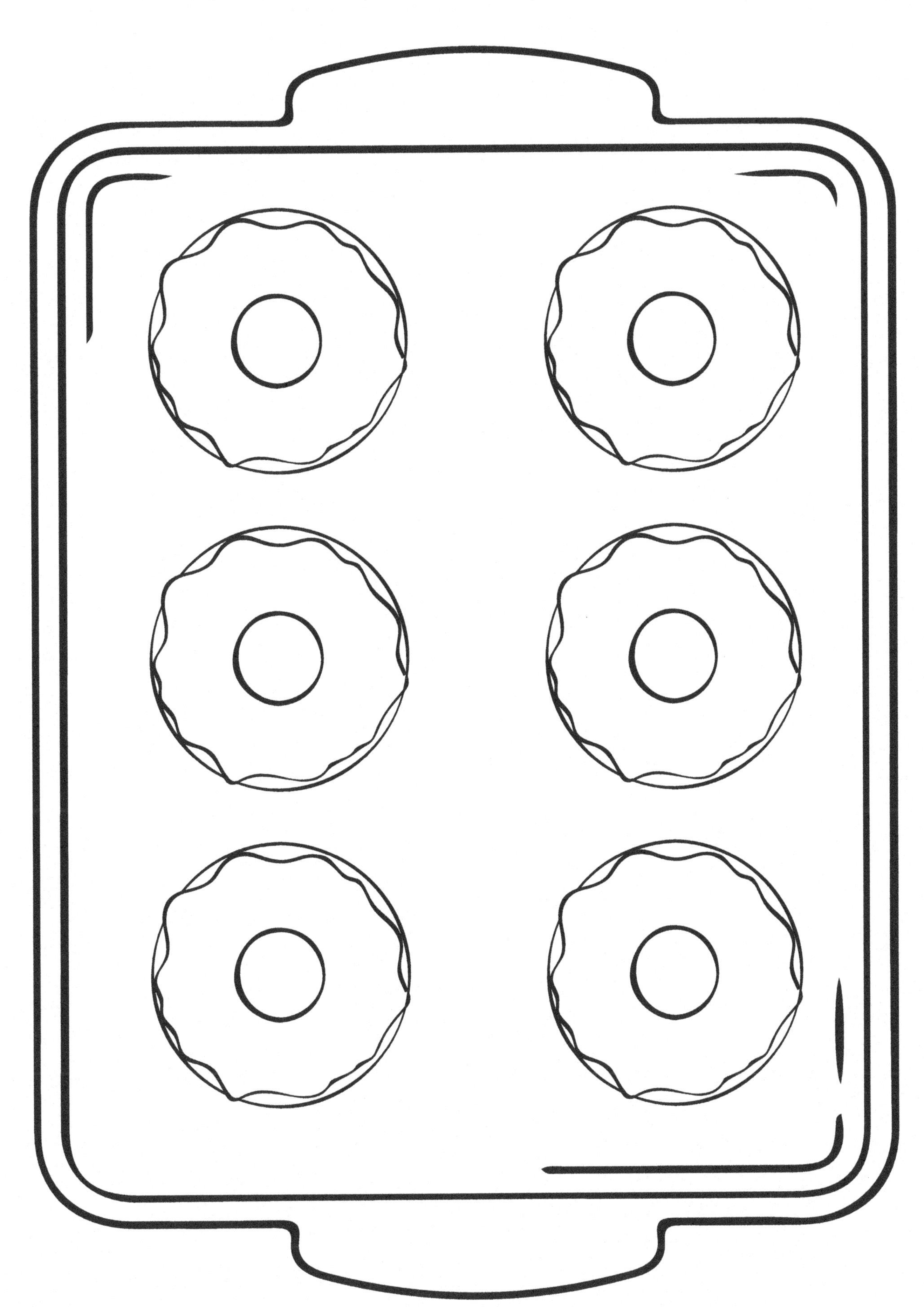

WHICH BALLOON BELONGS TO THE UNICORN?

DRAW A LINE TO MATCH THE CUPCAKES WITH THEIR SHADOWS.

OUT FOR A RIDE!

HELLO MY NAME IS ______________________

AND MY FAVORITE ICE CREAM FLAVOR IS ______________________

USE THE GRID TO
DRAW THE PICTURE.

CONNECT THE DOTS

1–11

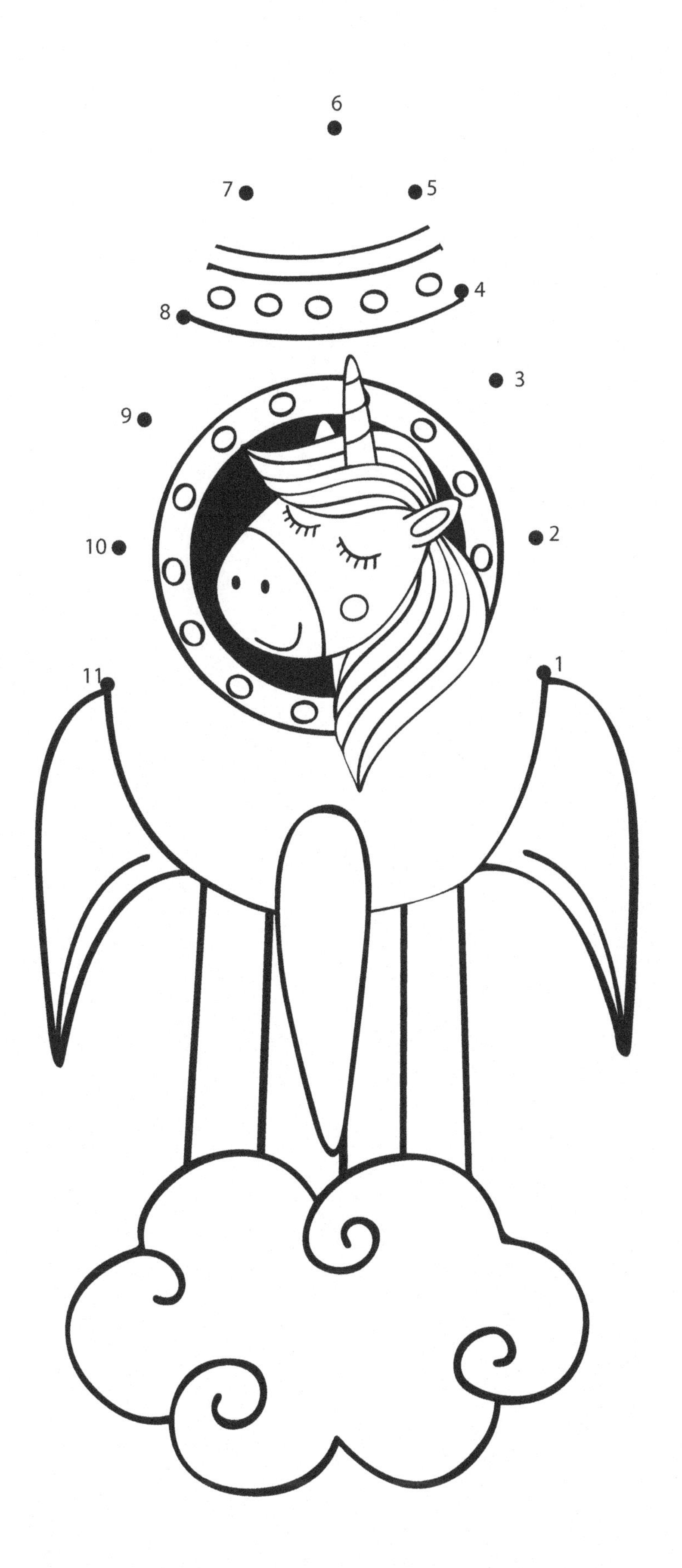

WHAT PRETTY FLOWERS!

FIND THE 4 DIFFERENCES IN THESE TWO SCENES.

HOW MANY BUTTERFLIES DO YOU COUNT?

ANSWER: 5

Use your imagination!

DRAW A PICTURE OF YOURSELF WITH THE UNICORN.

WORD SEARCH

FIND THE UNICORN FRIENDS BELOW!

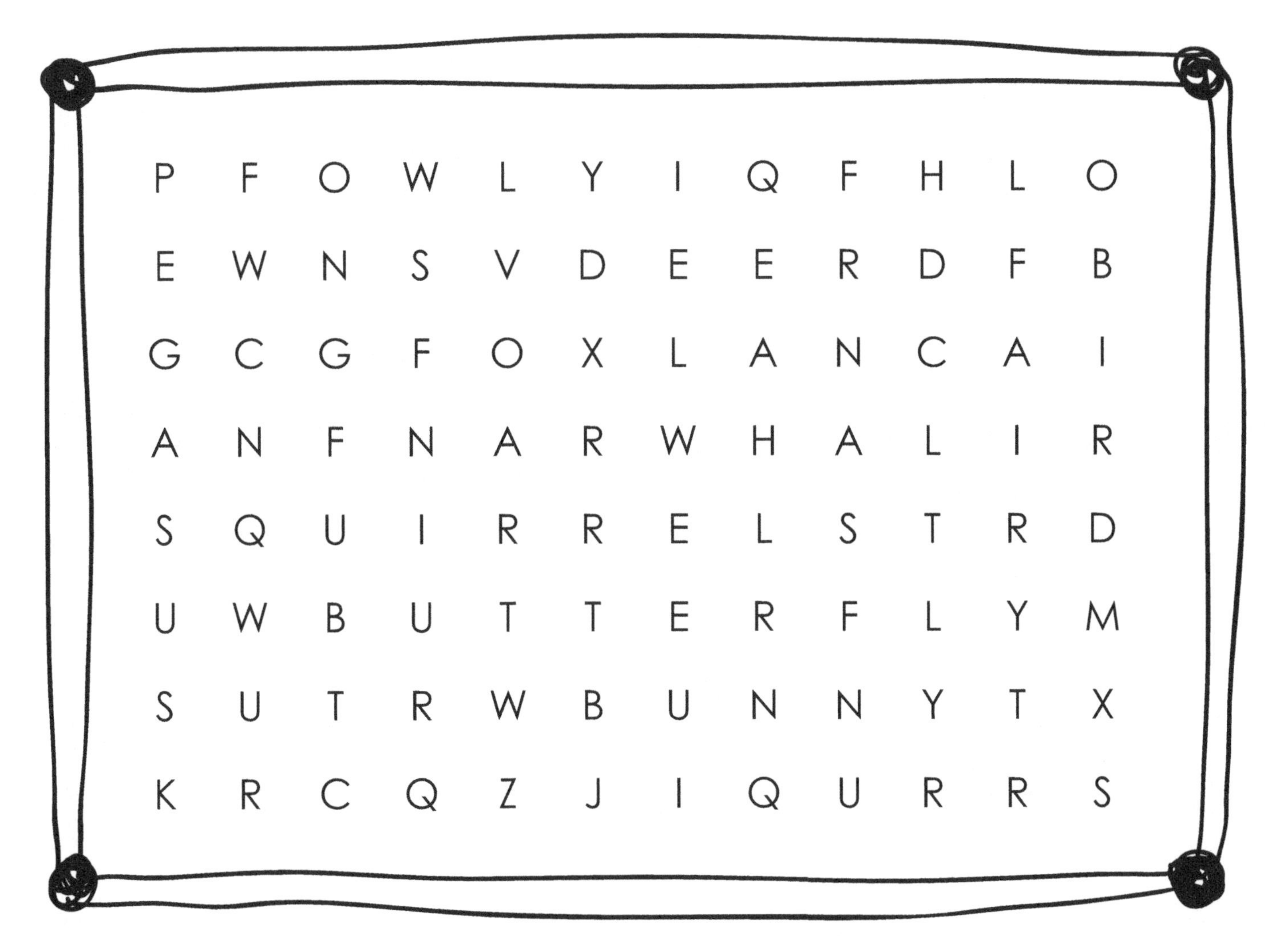

- BIRD
- BUNNY
- BUTTERFLY
- DEER
- FAIRY
- FOX
- NARWHAL
- OWL
- PEGASUS
- SQUIRREL

HELLO MY NAME IS
AND MY MAGICAL POWER IS

YOU'RE OUT OF THIS WORLD!

CONNECT THE DOTS

1–19

HELP THE UNICORN FIND HIS WAY TO THE CASTLE.

USE THE GRID TO DRAW THE PICTURE.

MAMA & BABY!

Use your imagination!

DECORATE THE CUPCAKES FOR A UNICORN BIRTHDAY PARTY.

WORD SEARCH

FIND THE UNICORN'S FAVORITE SNACKS BELOW!

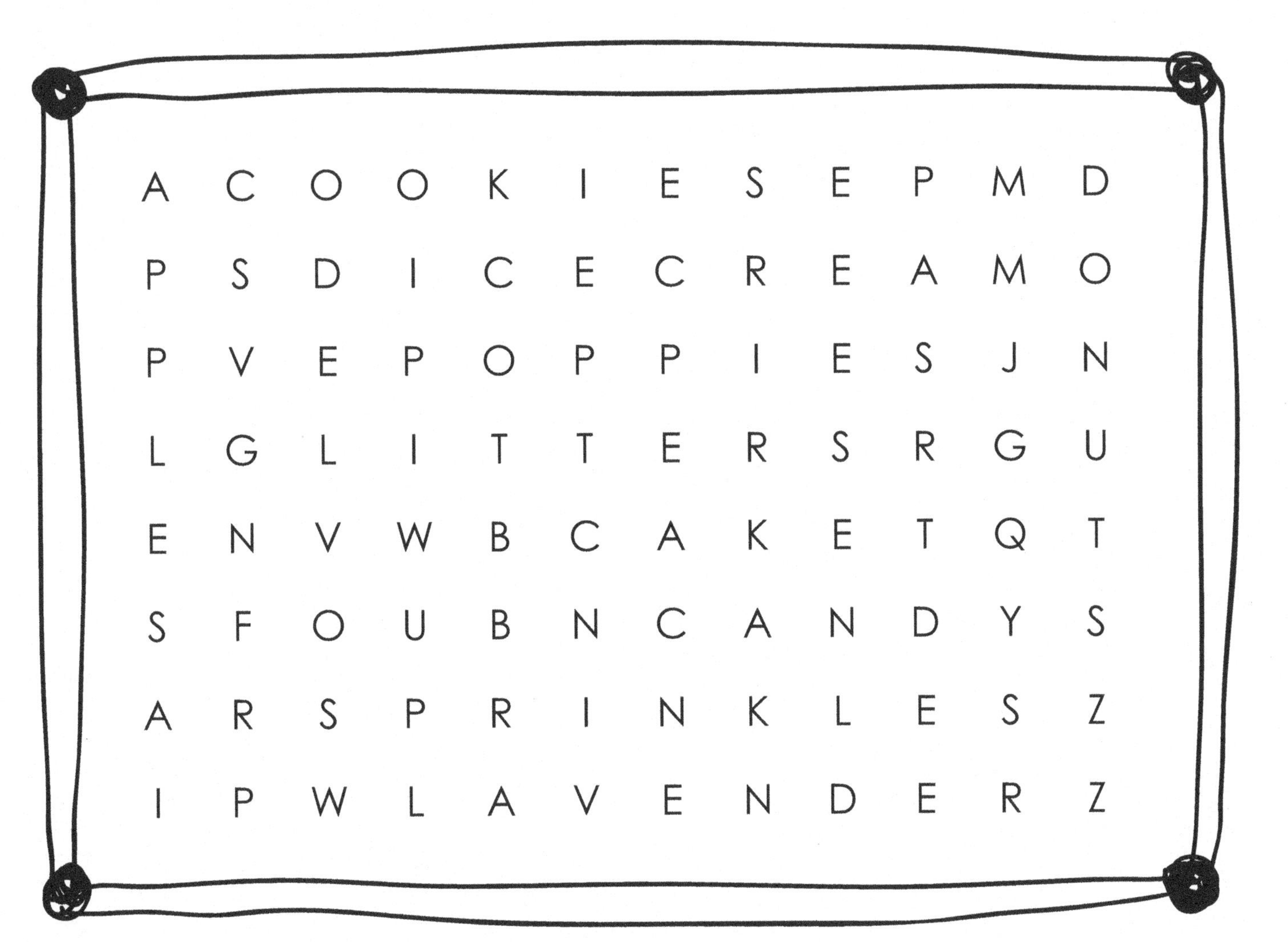

APPLES
CAKE
CANDY
COOKIES
DONUTS
GLITTER
ICE CREAM
LAVENDER
POPPIES
SPRINKLES

HELLO, BUNNY FRIEND!

DRAW A LINE TO MATCH THE UNICORNS WITH THEIR SHADOWS.

HELLO MY NAME IS ____________________

AND I LIKE TO ____________________

CONNECT THE DOTS

1–15

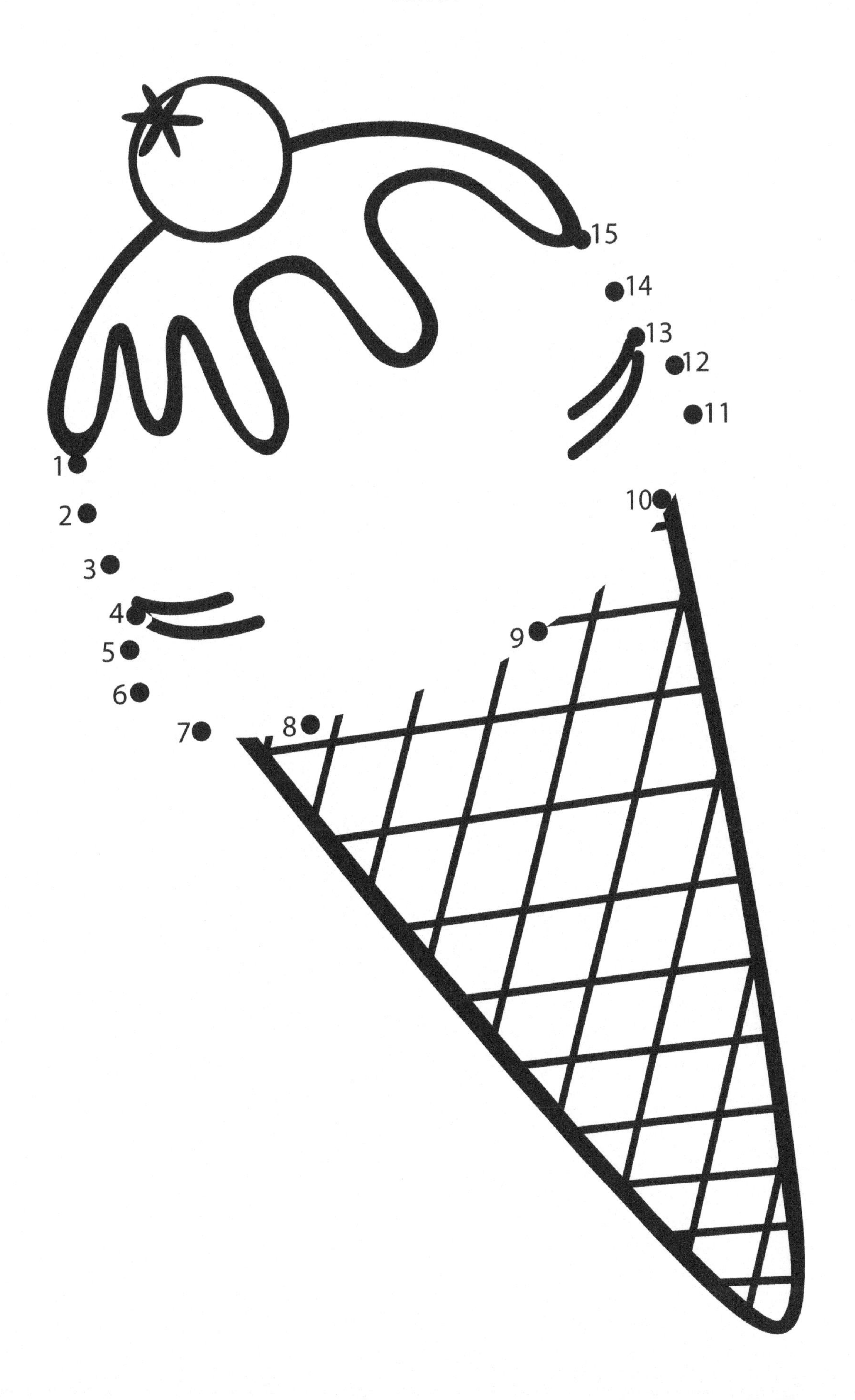

USE THE GRID TO
DRAW THE PICTURE.

REACH FOR THE STARS!

HELLO MY NAME IS ______________________________

AND MY BEST FRIEND IS ______________________________

WORD SEARCH

FIND THE UNICORN'S FAVORITE FLOWERS BELOW!

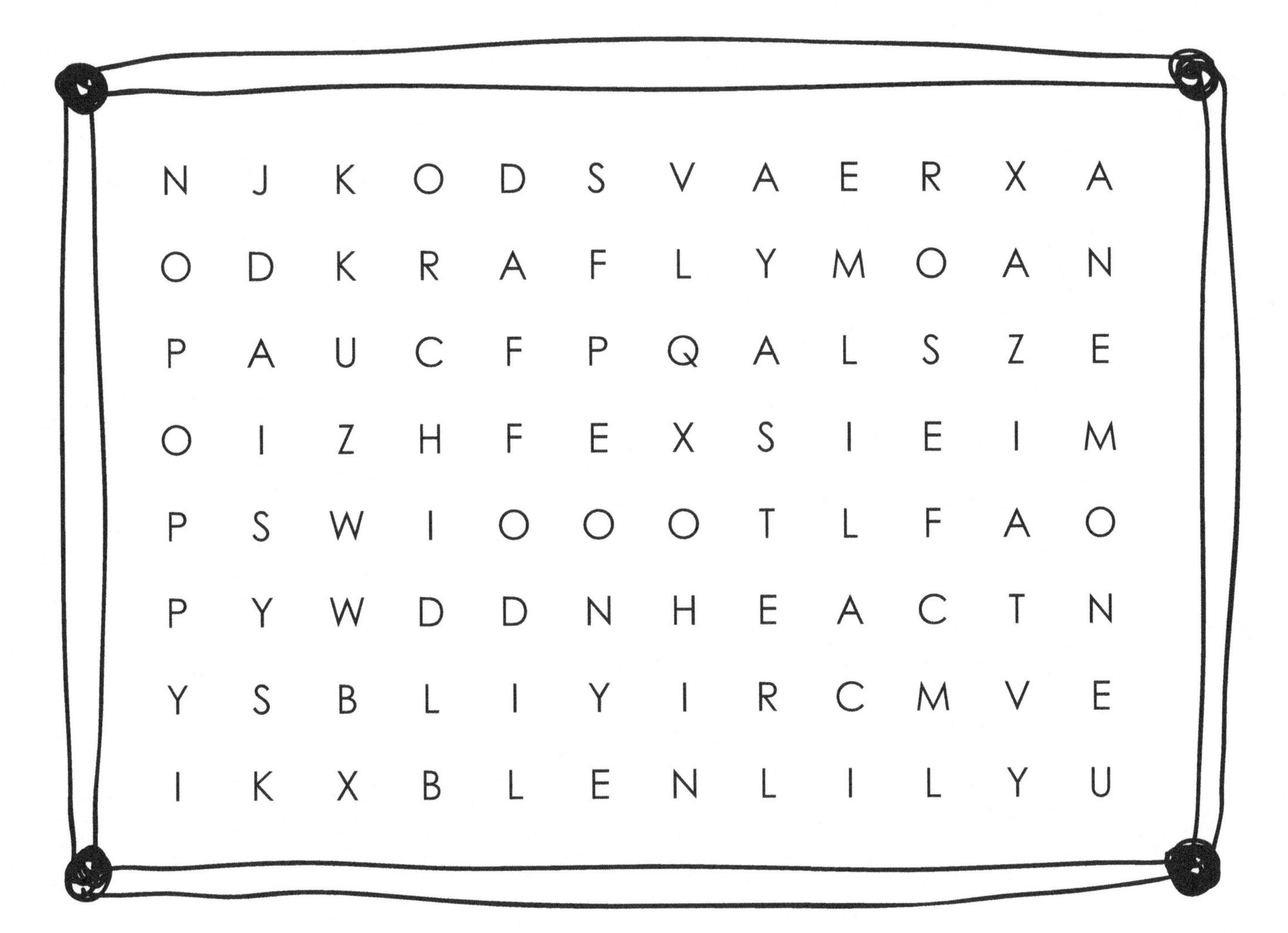

ANEMONE
ASTER
DAFFODIL
DAISY
LILAC
LILY
ORCHID
PEONY
POPPY
ROSE

WHAT A BEAUTIFUL CASTLE!

Use your imagination!

DRAW YOURSELF A CROWN TO WEAR TO THE ROYAL UNICORN BALL.

 DRAW A LINE TO MATCH THE CROWNS WITH THEIR SHADOWS.

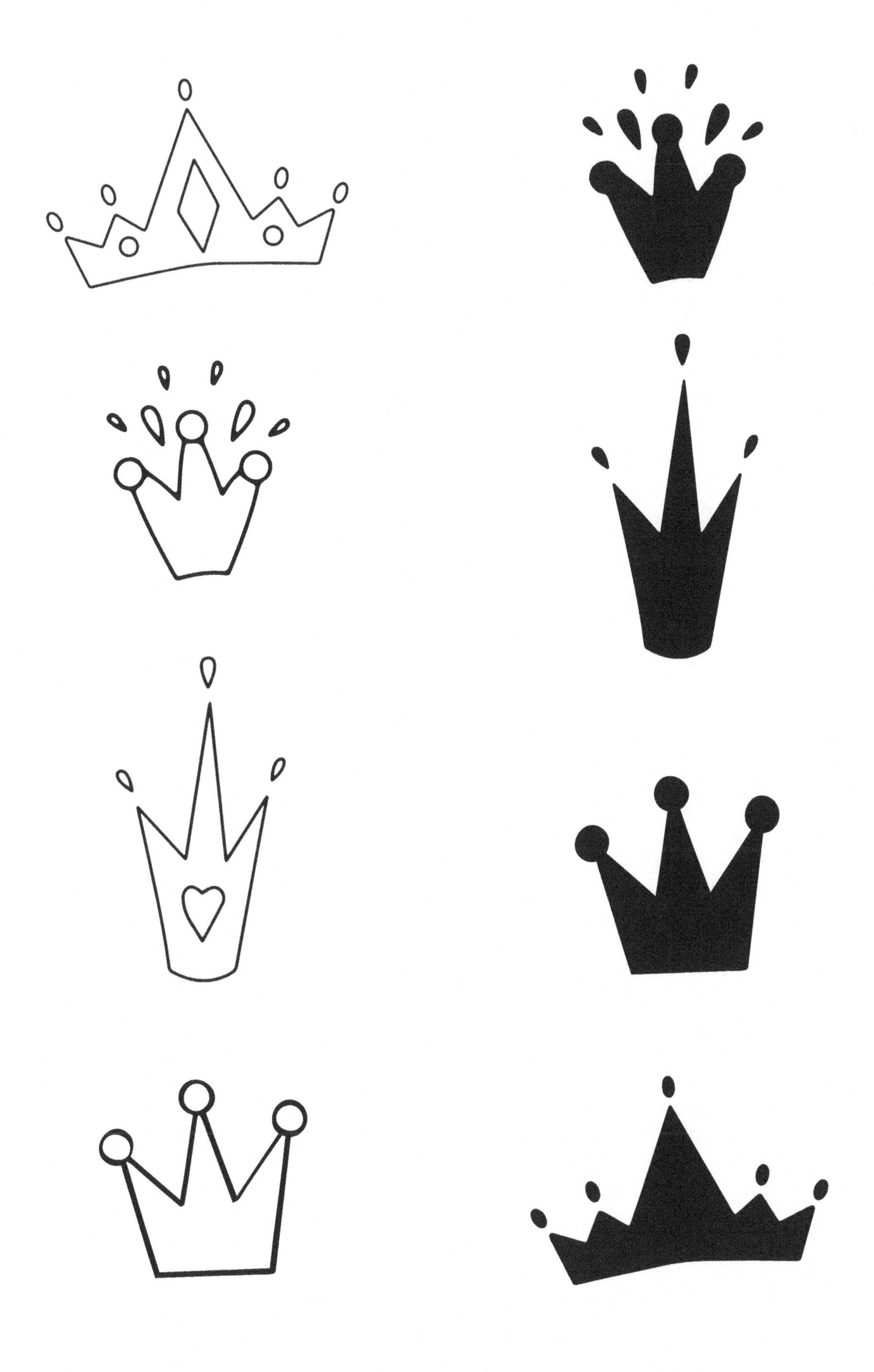

HOW MANY STARS DO YOU COUNT?

HELLO MY NAME IS ______________________________

AND MY FAVORITE ACTIVITY IS ______________________________

Made in the USA
Monee, IL
02 April 2020

24480689R00050